Good Ol' CHARLIE BROWN

Books by Charles M. Schulz

Peanuts
More Peanuts
Good Grief, More Peanuts!
Good Ol' Charlie Brown
Snoopy
You're Out of Your Mind, Charlie Brown!
But We Love You, Charlie Brown
Peanuts Revisited
Go Fly a Kite, Charlie Brown
Peanuts Every Sunday
It's a Dog's Life, Charlie Brown
You Can't Win, Charlie Brown
Snoopy, Come Home
You Can Do It, Charlie Brown
We're Right Behind You, Charlie Brown
As You Like It, Charlie Brown
Sunday's Fun Day, Charlie Brown
You Need Help, Charlie Brown
Snoopy and the Red Baron
The Unsinkable Charlie Brown
You'll Flip, Charlie Brown
You're Something Else, Charlie Brown
Peanuts Treasury
You're You, Charlie Brown
You've Had It, Charlie Brown
Snoopy and His Sopwith Camel
A Boy Named Charlie Brown
You're Out of Sight, Charlie Brown

Weekly Reader Children's Book Club presents

Good Ol'
CHARLIE BROWN

A NEW PEANUTS BOOK

by Charles M. Schulz

HOLT, RINEHART AND WINSTON

New York   Chicago   San Francisco

SIGH

NOBODY'S HAPPY WHERE THEY ARE...

WELL, HI!

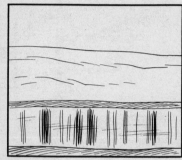

SCHULZ

GOOD GRIEF! I THINK I FROZE MY STOMACH!

SCHULZ

SOMETIMES THAT CHARLIE BROWN IS PRETTY CLEVER..

THREE BIG BOYS FROM THE SECOND GRADE WERE CHASING HIM TODAY...

HE RAN AND RAN AND RAN, BUT THEY KEPT GETTING CLOSER AND CLOSER AND CLOSER...

SUDDENLY HE ORGANIZED A DISCUSSION GROUP!

SCHULZ

I'M TRYING TO LEARN TO PLAY ALL OF THE BEETHOVEN SONATAS..

GEE...IF YOU **DO** LEARN TO PLAY THEM ALL, WHAT WILL YOU **WIN**?

I WON'T **WIN** ANYTHING!

YOU WON'T?

WHAT'S THE SENSE IN DOING SOMETHING IF YOU DON'T WIN A PRIZE?

SCHULZ

I THOUGHT I TOLD YOU TO STOP THAT DANCING?! YOU HAVE NO RIGHT TO BE SO HAPPY!!! NOW, STOP IT! DO YOU HEAR ME?!

SCHULZ

WHAT'S THAT DOTTED LINE ON YOUR BLANKET FOR, LINUS?

RIP!

HAPPINESS SHOULD BE SHARED!

SCHULZ

I'M GOING TO HAVE A PARTY, CHARLIE BROWN, AND I'M NOT GOING TO INVITE YOU...

NYAHH, NYAHH, NYAHH!

I DON'T MIND NOT BEING INVITED TO HER PARTY...

IT'S THOSE 'NYAHHS' THAT GET ME!

SCHULZ

I'VE BEEN WATCHING THESE BUGS, CHARLIE BROWN...

YOU SEE, THIS ONE BUG HERE IS ABOUT TO LEAVE HOME..HE'S BEEN SAYING GOOD-BYE TO ALL HIS FRIENDS

SUDDENLY THIS LITTLE GIRL BUG COMES RUNNING UP, AND TRIES TO PERSUADE HIM NOT TO LEAVE...

IF YOU'RE GOING TO BE A GOOD 'BUG-WATCHER' YOU HAVE TO HAVE LOTS OF IMAGINATION!

SCHULZ

"BEETHOVEN TOOK THIS REBUFF VERY HARD."

"FOR WEEKS AFTERWARD HE WAS EXTREMELY UNHAPPY...."

HOW COULD ANYONE BE BEETHOVEN AND NOT BE HAPPY?

DO YOU THINK THE WORLD IS GETTING SMALLER, CHARLIE BROWN?

OH, YES...THE AIRPLANE HAS MADE IT MUCH SMALLER..

OH, DON'T BE SO DUMB... THE AIRPLANE HASN'T HAD ANYTHING TO DO WITH IT...IT'S THE **PEOPLE!**

MILLIONS OF 'EM! AND THEY'RE MAKING THE WORLD SMALLER BECAUSE THEY'RE WALKING ALL OVER IT, AND THEY'RE **WEARING IT DOWN!**

LUCY, HOW DID YOU EVER GET TO BE SUCH A FUSS-BUDGET?

I'LL HAVE YOU KNOW I STUDIED HARD! LOOK AT ALL THOSE BOOKS.. EACH ONE A COURSE IN ITSELF...

"FROM RAGS TO FUSS-BUDGET".. "THE POWER OF POSITIVE FUSSING".. "GREAT FUSS-BUDGETS OF OUR TIME".."

AND HERE'S ONE OF MY REAL FAVORITES..." I WAS A FUSS-BUDGET FOR THE F.B.I."!

SCHULZ

IT'S NO USE!

I CAN'T SHOOT WHEN HE'S SITTING THERE! HE MAKES ME NERVOUS!

ALL RIGHT, I'LL SEE WHAT I CAN DO...

YOU HEARD HIM, SNOOPY...YOU'LL JUST HAVE TO GET DOWN..

SCHULZ

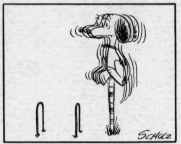

WELL?! WHO'S GOING TO OPEN THE DOOR?!

YOU THINK YOU'RE SMART JUST BECAUSE YOU'RE OLDER THAN I AM!

YOU JUST **HAPPENED** TO BE BORN FIRST THAT'S ALL!!! YOU WERE JUST **LUCKY**!!

I DIDN'T **ASK** TO BE BORN SECOND!

I DIDN'T EVEN GET A CHANCE TO FILL OUT AN APPLICATION!

LEAVES ARE A FASCINATING STUDY, LINUS..

MOST PEOPLE THINK THAT THE LEAVES JUST FALL OFF WHEN AUTUMN COMES...

MY STOMACH!

BUT THE **TRUTH** IS THAT THEY ALL **JUMP** OFF BEFORE THE **SQUIRRELS** CAN GET 'EM!

THAT DID IT! MOVE OVER, CHARLIE BROWN..

WE HAVE TO BE NICE TO SNOOPY... THIS IS **HIS** DAY!

I THINK YOU'D BETTER LOOK AT YOUR CALENDAR AGAIN, LUCY...

FEBRUARY SECOND..'GROUND-HOG DAY'...WELL, I'LL BE!

I'M SORRY, SNOOPY... I THOUGHT IT SAID, 'GROUND-**DOG** DAY'..

'AT THE CONCLUSION OF THE SYMPHONY THE AUDIENCE STOOD UP, AND CHEERED...'

'BEETHOVEN, HOWEVER, BECAUSE OF HIS DEAFNESS, COULD NOT HEAR THEM, AND BECAUSE HIS BACK WAS TO THE AUDIENCE, COULD NOT SEE THEM..'

'WITH TEARS IN HER EYES ONE OF THE SINGERS LED BEETHOVEN TO THE EDGE OF THE STAGE WHERE HE COULD SEE THE CHEERING PEOPLE..'

SOB

SCHULZ

SEE, LINUS? YOU TAKE A PIECE OF PAPER...FOLD A LITTLE HERE...

..TEAR A LITTLE THERE, AND BEHOLD! YOU HAVE A BOAT!

?

SCHULZ

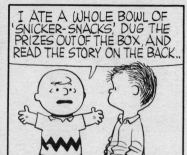

A KANGAROO! THAT'S WHAT I'D LIKE TO BE! BOY, I'D GO JUMPING ALL OVER THE PLACE...

LISTEN!

WHAT'S THE MATTER?

I THOUGHT I HEARD SOMETHING GO, "BWANG"....

YOU'RE LOSING YOUR MIND, CHARLIE BROWN!

BWANG! BWANG! BWANG!

SCHULZ

'THE KANGAROO IS AN ANIMAL FOUND ONLY IN AUSTRALIA'

DON'T BE TOO SURE..

WHAT DO YOU MEAN, DON'T BE TOO SURE?!

JUST WHAT I SAID, LUCY.. DON'T BE TOO SURE...

BWANG! BWANG! BWANG!

SCHULZ

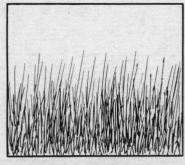

AAK!

SNOOPY COULD NEVER BE A HUNTING DOG... TALL WEEDS GIVE HIM CLAUSTROPHOBIA!

"CLAUSTROPHOBIA, AN ABNORMAL FEAR OF BEING IN AN ENCLOSED PLACE"

YOU'D THINK THERE'D BE SOME MENTION OF "WEED-CLAUSTROPHOBIA", WOULDN'T YOU?

KLUNK! **BUMP!BUMP!**
bumpety-bump CRASH!!

WHAT IN THE WORLD WAS **THAT**?!

I GUESS IT WAS SNOOPY...IF HE DOESN'T LIKE HIS SUPPER, HE JUST PUSHES IT DOWNSTAIRS!

SCHULZ

'PIG-PEN', HAVE YOU EVER HEARD THAT OLD SAYING?

WHAT OLD SAYING?

'CLEANLINESS IS NEXT TO GODLINESS'

OH, YES... MANY TIMES..

THEN WHY DON'T YOU FOLLOW IT?

BECAUSE WITH ME, CHARLIE BROWN, CLEANLINESS IS NEXT TO IMPOSSIBLE!

SCHULZ

AHCHOO!

CHARLIE BROWN, WOULD YOU LIKE TO COME TO A PARTY SOMETIME NEXT WEEK?

WHY, YES, I'D LIKE THAT VERY MUCH..

I THOUGHT YOU WOULD...BUT I DOUBT IF I'LL INVITE YOU ANYWAY..

THE ONLY TROUBLE WITH LIVING IN THESE NEW HOUSING DEVELOPMENTS IS THERE ARE NO TREES TO HIT YOUR HEAD AGAINST!

SCHULZ

GEE! IT DIDN'T EVEN BREAK..

NOW, YOU KNOW WHAT YOU'RE GOING TO DO TOMORROW NIGHT, DON'T YOU?

SURE.. I JUST GO UP TO THESE DIFFERENT HOUSES, RING THEIR DOORBELLS AND THEN SHOUT, **"TRICKS OR TREATS!"**

SAY, BY THE WAY... THERE'S NO LAW AGAINST THAT, IS THERE?

OF COURSE NOT..

I WOULDN'T WANT TO DO ANYTHING THAT MIGHT AROUSE THE F.B.I.!